VINTAGE
COLOURING BOOK

VINTAGE
COLOURING BOOK

ARCTURUS

ARCTURUS

This edition published in 2015 by Arcturus Publishing Limited
26/27 Bickels Yard, 151–153 Bermondsey Street,
London SE1 3HA

ISBN: 978-1-78404-633-0
AD004690NT

Printed in Spain

Introduction

More and more adults are discovering the health benefits of colouring. This gentle activity not only occupies the hands, it also relaxes the mind and body and helps to banish negative thoughts. It unlocks creativity and helps you enter a freer state of being.

The Vintage Colouring Book contains a gorgeous selection of designs, ranging from Victoriana to Art Deco and Pop Art. All you need to get started are the most basic artist's materials and soon you will be producing your own beautiful artworks.

So grab those pencils or pens, and let the colour in!

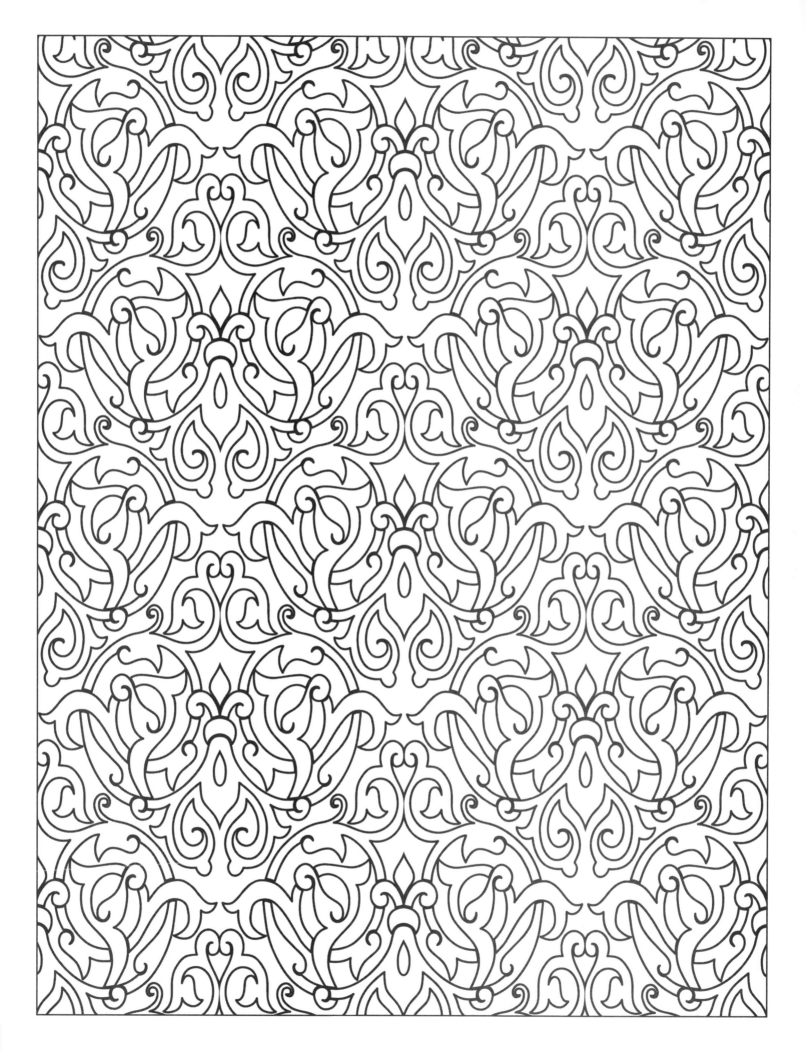

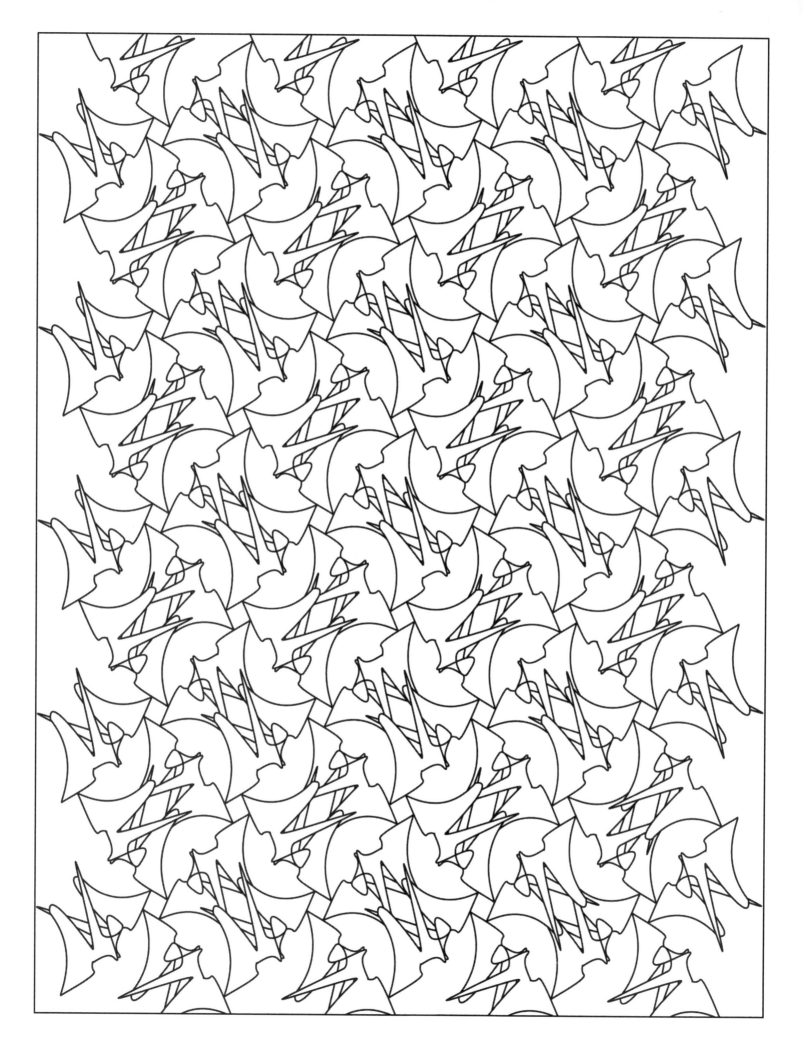